Tim Hawkins

FIRST STEPS

STARTING TO FOLLOW JESUS

PO Box A287
Sydney South NSW 1235
Australia
ISBN 978-1-875861-45-3
National Library of Australia

Published 1992. Reprinted 1996. Revised 1997.
Reprinted 1999, 2000, 2001, 2004, 2009, 2011.
Redesigned 2013.
© Tim Hawkins 1992

Typesetting and design: Bethany Abbottsmith
Artwork: Ritchie Priyana
Project manager: Derek Nelson
Managing editor: Natasha Percy

CONTENTS

STUDY 1

WHAT'S HAPPENED TO ME?

I'M A BRAND NEW PERSON!

2 Corinthians 5:17

What does God do for you when you become a Christian?

_____

_____

_____

_____

_____

_____

I'M GOD'S FRIEND

2 Romans 5:8-10

VERSE 9

So when you become a Christian, what are two of the things that Jesus death will do for you?

i.

ii.

VERSE 8

What has God done for you that shows how much he loves you?

VERSE 10

What is another change that happens when you become a Christian?

JESUS

3 Ephesians 1:4-7

VERSE 4 What had God already done for you even before the world was made?

_____

_____

_____

_____

VERSE 5 What else does God make you become?

_____

_____

_____

_____

VERSE 7 So what does Jesus' death do for us?

_____

_____

_____

_____

_____

CHOSEN! ▶ CHILD OF GOD ▶ FORGIVEN

MADE ALIVE

4 Ephesians 1:13
What does God give you when you believe in Christ?

5 Ephesians 2:4-5
What did God do for us while we were spiritually dead?

6 Ephesians 2:10
So now that you've become a Christian, what has God already prepared for you to do?

7 Isaiah: 55:7

So if someone really wants to follow God, what do they need to do?

LEAVE _____

CHANGE _____

TURN TO _____

8

If I'm really going to live the way a Christian should, these are some changes I need to make in my life:

_____

_____

_____

_____

_____

_____

_____

_____

I'VE GOT A BRAND NEW WAY TO LIVE!

9 This is what I think is the **BEST** thing about being a Christian:

_____
_____
_____
_____
_____
_____
_____

10 This is what I find the **HARDEST** about being a Christian:

_____
_____
_____
_____
_____

8

MY PRAYER TO GOD

Dear God,

_____

_____

_____

_____

_____

Your friend,

MEMORY VERSE

New life in Christ
2 CORINTHIANS 5:17

'Therefore, if anyone is in Christ,
the new creation has come:
The old has gone, the new is here!'

STUDY 2 YOU'RE IN THE FAMILY!

WHAT FAMILY?

GOD'S FAMILY!

 **1 John 3:1**

Because God's love for us is so great, what does he now call us?

_____

 **Hebrews 13:1**

If every Christian is one of God's children,
what should be our attitude to other Christians?

_____

_____

3 Hebrews 10:24-25

VERSE 24

As members of God's family what should we help each other to do?

VERSE 25

What must we make sure we don't give up?

VERSE 25

So what should we do for one another?

_____ _____ _____

_____ _____ _____

_____ _____ _____

_____ _____ _____

_____ _____ _____

_____

4 Matthew 18:20

What special promise does Jesus give when Christians meet together?

_____

_____

_____

_____

5 Romans 15:7

How should we treat other Christians?

_____

_____

_____

6 1 Thessalonians 5:12–13

How should you treat people who are your Christian leaders?

_____

_____

_____

7 ## Acts 2:42

This is the earliest record of what the first Christians did when they met together. List the four things they did:

i. _____

ii. _____

iii. _____

iv. _____

WE ALL GROW TOGETHER IN FELLOWSHIP

A group of Christians is described in the Bible as being like a single body. Every Christian there is part of that body. Every Christian is needed to make the body work properly. You can't just be a Christian by yourself. You need other Christians to help you, and they need you to help them.

8 Take time now to describe the Christian groups that you belong to.

Here are some of the groups where I meet with other Christians:

_____

_____

_____

_____

THE LAST QUESTION!

Here is something I can do so that I can have more valuable fellowship with other Christians:

_____

_____

_____

_____

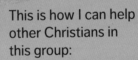

This is how I can help other Christians in this group:

_____

_____

This is how others in this group help me:

_____

_____

_____

MY PRAYER TO GOD

Dear God,

_____

_____

_____

_____

_____

_____

Your friend,

MEMORY VERSE

Fellowship together
HEBREWS 10:24–25

'... Let us consider how we may spur one another on toward love and good deeds, not giving up meeting together, as some are in the habit of doing, but encouraging one another— and all the more as you see the Day approaching.'

STUDY 3

LET'S LISTEN TO GOD!

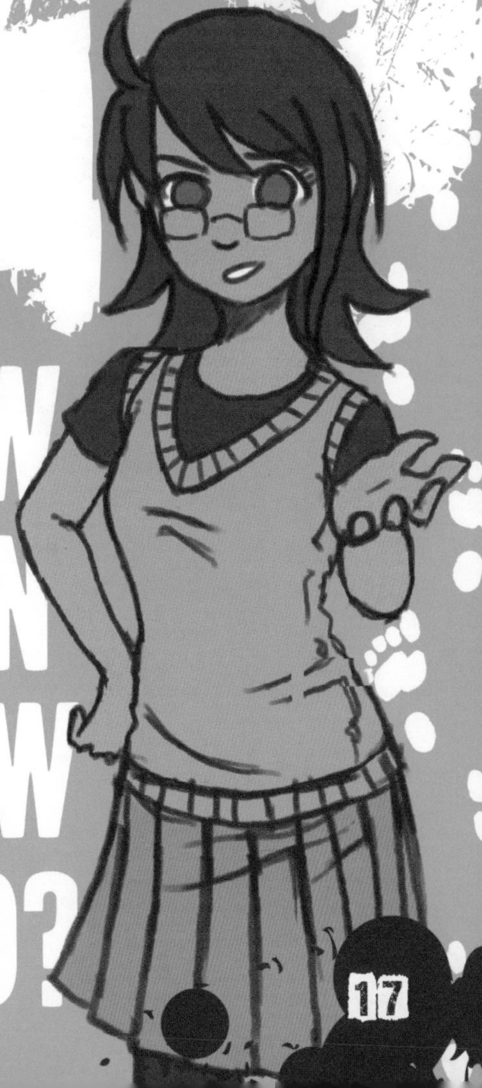

HOW CAN I KNOW GOD?

READ THE BIBLE

1 2 Timothy 3:16–17

VERSE 16

Where does all Scripture come from?

_____

_____

VERSE 17

What will the Bible do for the person who serves God?

_____

_____

_____

_____

What four things will the Bible do in your life?

i. _____

_____

ii. _____

_____

iii. _____

_____

iv. _____

_____

2 Psalm 19:7-8

VERSE	What the word of God is	What the word of God will do for you
7		
7		
8		
8		

1. TEACHING THE TRUTH: shows you the way to go.

2. SHOWING WHAT'S WRONG: shows you when you're going wrong.

God's way

4. GIVING DIRECTION: shows you how to keep going the right way.

3. CORRECTING MISTAKES: shows you how to get it right again.

19

3 Psalm 119:9-11

How can you keep your life pure?

What two things should you try
to do with all your heart?

i.

ii.

What will help you not to sin against God?

BIG
NEWS!

Matthew 7:24-27

	WISE MAN	FOOLISH MAN
What did he build his house on?		
What happened when the storm came?		
Who does Jesus say this house-builder represents?		

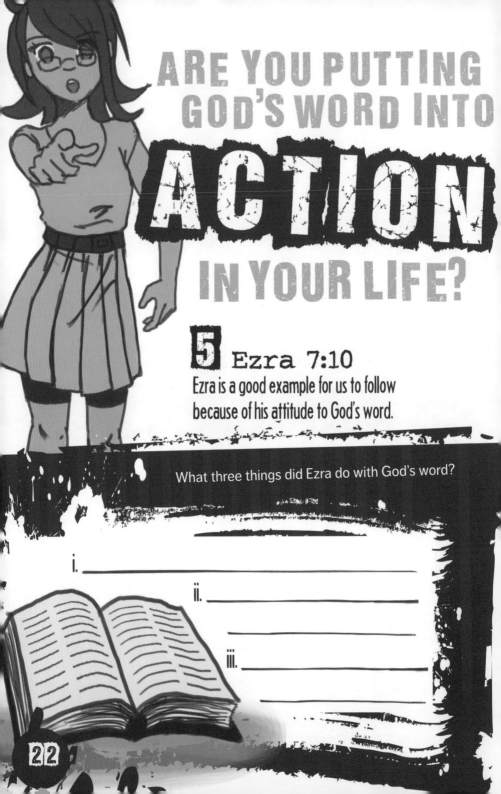

ARE YOU PUTTING GOD'S WORD INTO ACTION IN YOUR LIFE?

5 Ezra 7:10

Ezra is a good example for us to follow because of his attitude to God's word.

What three things did Ezra do with God's word?

i. _____

ii. _____

iii. _____

6 What do you find usually stops you from spending time reading the Bible?

_____

_____

_____

_____

7 Each week, how often would you spend time reading the Bible:

by yourself? _____

with others? _____

Dive into the Scriptures!

8 What can you start doing so that you will grow to understand God's word better?

_____

_____

_____

_____

23

MY PRAYER TO GOD

Dear God,

_____

_____

_____

_____

_____

Your friend,

MEMORY VERSE

All Scripture

2 TIMOTHY 3:16–17

'All Scripture is God-breathed and is useful
for teaching, rebuking, correcting and training
in righteousness, so that the servant of God
may be thoroughly equipped for every good work.'

STUDY

4 LET'S TALK WITH GOD!

WHY PRAY?

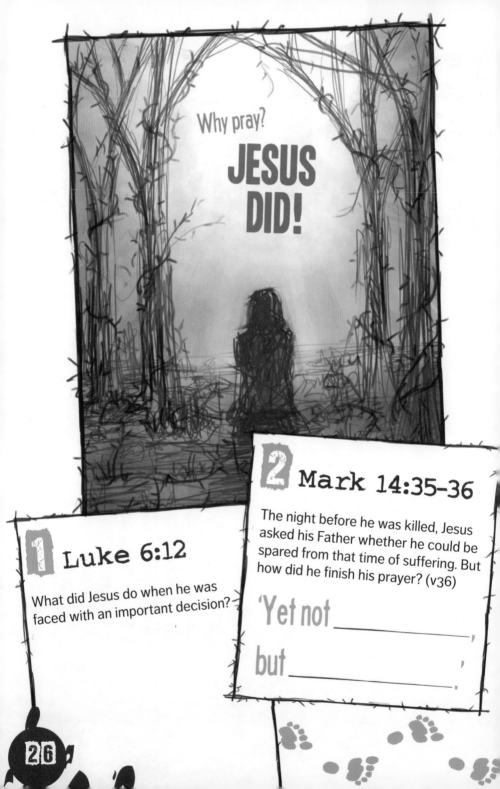

Why pray?

JESUS DID!

2 Mark 14:35–36

The night before he was killed, Jesus asked his Father whether he could be spared from that time of suffering. But how did he finish his prayer? (v36)

'Yet not _____,

but _____.'

1 Luke 6:12

What did Jesus do when he was faced with an important decision?

GOD GOD

GOD WANTS US TO PRAY

 Philippians 4:6-7

VERSE 6

What should we do instead
of worrying about things?

_____

_____

VERSE 6

What attitude should we have
when we ask God for things?

_____

_____

VERSE 7

What will God do for us when we
turn things over to him in prayer?

_____

_____

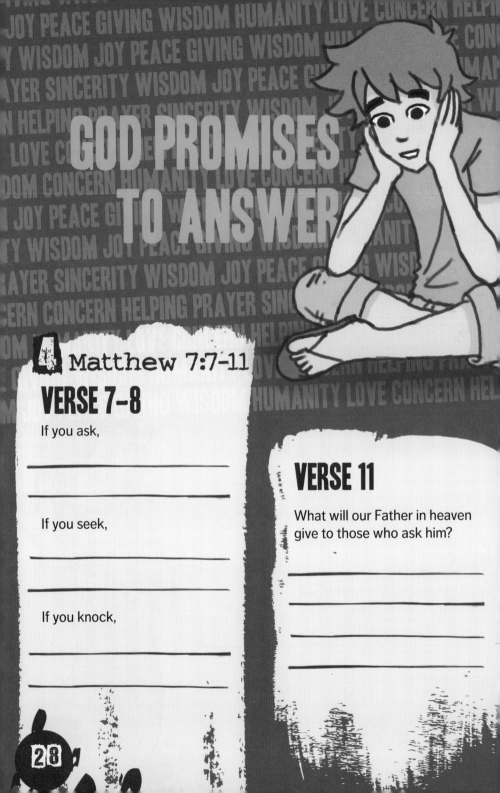

GOD PROMISES TO ANSWER

4 Matthew 7:7-11

VERSE 7-8

If you ask,

_____

_____

If you seek,

_____

_____

If you knock,

_____

_____

VERSE 11

What will our Father in heaven give to those who ask him?

_____

_____

_____

_____

28

WILL GOD ALWAYS SAY YES?

 6 What will sometimes stop our prayers from being answered the way we want?

James 4:3

_____

_____

_____

Psalm 66:18

_____

_____

_____

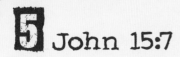 **5** John 15:7

What does Jesus say to do if we want God to answer our prayers?

_____

_____

_____

_____

7 What do you find usually stops you from spending time talking with God in prayer?

_____

_____

_____

_____

_____

8 Each week, how often would you spend praying:

by yourself? _____

with others? _____

9 When you do pray to God, what sorts of things do you normally say to him

_____

_____

_____

_____

GOD'S ANSWERS

God has promised to answer all our prayers.
But he WON'T always answer them the way WE WANT!
He will answer them the way that he knows is BEST!

 God will say **YES** to the things he knows will be good for us.

 God will say **NO** to the things he knows will not be good for us.

 God will say **WAIT** to the things he knows we are not yet ready for.

HOW TO PRAY

There are many different ways to pray.
Here are four important ways:

I love you ...
Tell God why you love him and how much you love him.

Thanks ...
Thank God for all the great things he has done for you.

Sorry ...
Tell God about the wrong things you've done and the ways you have let him down.

Please ...
Ask God to help other people and to help you.

MY PRAYER TO GOD

Dear God,

I love you ————————————

————————————

Thanks ————————————

————————————

Sorry ————————————

Please ————————————

Your friend,

MEMORY VERSE

God answers prayer
JOHN 15:7

'If you remain in me
and my words remain in you,
ask whatever you wish,
and it will be done for you.'

STUDY 5

A NEW WAY TO LIVE

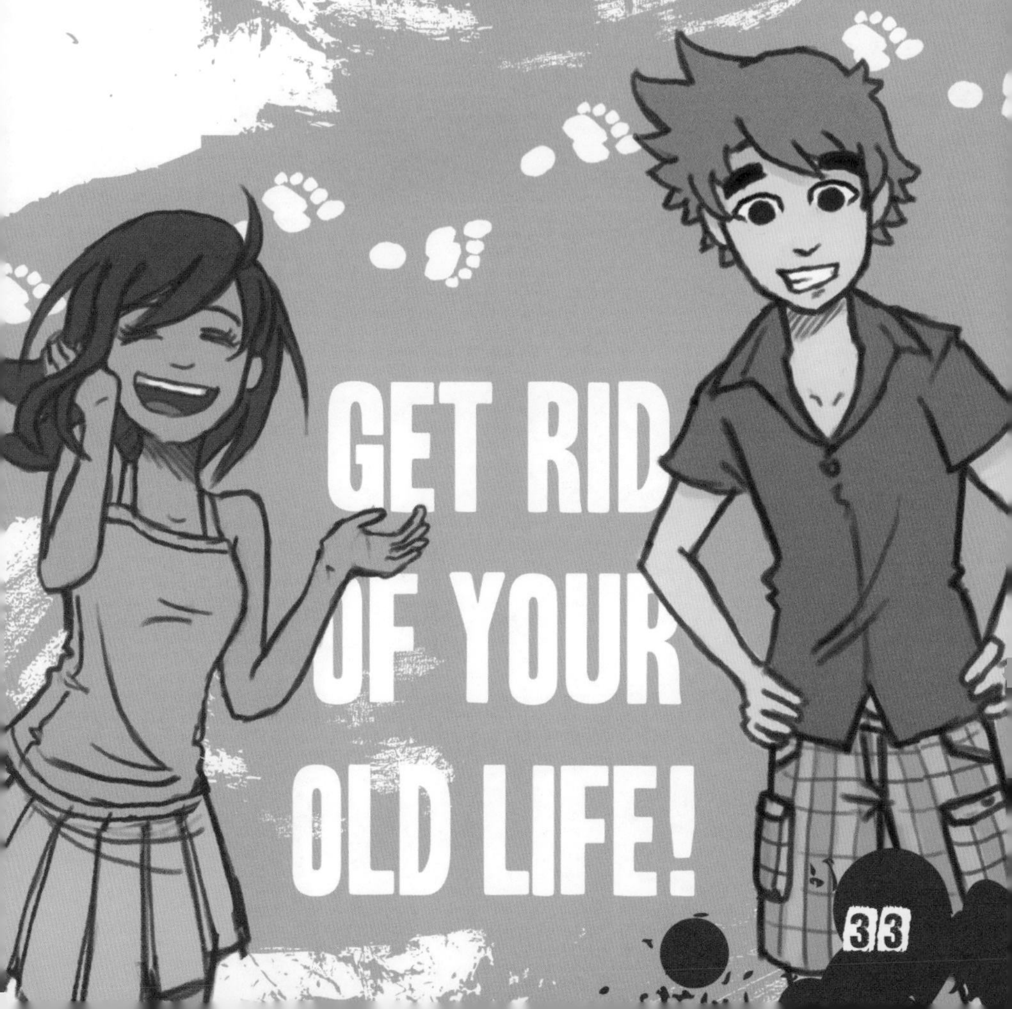

GET RID OF YOUR OLD LIFE!

1 Ephesians 5:8-11

VERSE 8 Now that God has brought us into the 'light' by making us his people, what are we meant to be like?

_____

_____

VERSE 10 What should we learn to do?

_____

_____

VERSE 11 What should we have nothing to do with?

_____

_____

2 John 14:15

What does Jesus say we will do if we really love him?

_____

_____

_____

_____

3 Ephesians 4:22-24

VERSE 22 When you become a Christian, what are you meant to get rid of?

_____

_____

_____

_____

_____

_____

VERSES 23-24 What are you meant to replace this with?

_____

_____

4 Ephesians 5:1-2

VERSE 1 When you become one of God's children, what must you do?

_____

_____

_____

VERSE 2 How are you meant to live your life?

_____

_____

_____

5 1 John 3:18

What sort of love are we meant
to show to others?

_____

_____

_____

_____

6 Galatians 6:10

Who are you meant to do good to?

_____

_____

_____

_____

7 Matthew 5:16

What should be the result of people
seeing the good things you do?

LET'S PUT IT INTO ACTION!

AREAS IN MY LIFE	WHAT I HAVE TO STOP...
With my non-Christian friends	
With my family	
With my Christian friends	
In what I think about	
In my relationship with God	